Dear Nature,

John Newling

Dear Nature,
John Newling

Beam Editions

John Newling
Midlands, UK

Nature
The Earth

8th January 2018

Dear Nature,

I have always loved the unknowns of you.
But can we ever truly be together?

Yours,
John

John Newling
Midlands, UK

Nature
The Earth

9ᵗʰ January 2018

Dear Nature,

It has been a while but I feel moved to say how sorry I am that our relationship has become so problematic in recent times.

It seems us humans have been affecting your effects for many years now. I think we always wanted to control your wonder to our benefit. But to realise the agents of such control may lead to our extinction has confused and unsettled our relationship with you.

What to do?

Yours,
John

John Newling
Midlands, UK

Nature
The Earth

10th January 2018

Dear Nature,

We have been lovers.
We made deities from your wonders.
We worshipped you; laid our fears at your feet.
We thought that we needed you to need us.
But wasn't that just some way of seeking control?

Maybe we find it hard to accept that you are the most
powerful and complex set of relationships we can
encounter; perhaps we got jealous of all your other affairs.

In our rush to evolve, with our fights and flights, we
have got lost amongst our own conceits; spinning such a
terrible storm.

I am sorry.

What to do?

Yours,
John

John Newling
Midlands, UK

Nature
The Earth

11th January 2018

Dear Nature,

In the beginning farming was our evolutionary way. It fed us.
We learnt how to work your soils and follow your seasons.
We tried so hard to acknowledge your amazing ways. Ritual
after ritual constructed to try to guarantee your consistency; a
courtship of a kind, even love of a sort. But love dulls and we
slowly forgot you in our fever to move on. So many clearings,
so much damage.

Our conceit has been our desire for you to need us; to rule
over you. When such a desire seems to be reproached it
troubles our self-esteem; an unrequited wish.

All along we so wanted you to need us. Perhaps we could not
bear the thought that we needed you but you didn't need us.

We want to be loved.

Yours,
John

John Newling
Midlands, UK

Nature
The Earth

12th January 2018

Dear Nature,

In truth, we slowly ignored you as our need for something
greater than ourselves evolved the narratives and rituals
of our religions. We could only find some sort of trust in
reflections of ourselves.

But these are going now and we are left in the strangest
nihilism without purpose and feeling; disconnected. If only we
had understood that you were greater than we are. I think we
needed to be needed for something but forgot where we were.

Yours, trying to navigate our relationship,
John

John Newling
Midlands, UK

Nature   13th January 2018
The Earth

Dear Nature,

> *God blessed them and said to them, "Be fruitful
> and increase in number; fill the earth and subdue it.
> Rule over the fish in the sea and the birds in the sky
> and over every living creature that moves on the
> ground".*

This is my guilt and worry. We have filled the earth.
We have subdued it. We do rule over it.

What is the cost to ourselves of subduing all that we seem
to encounter? Yours is a vast history, ours is a blink in that
history. Perhaps that's where the hope lies in our geological
youth; we are young and still learning.

I am sorry.

Yours,
John

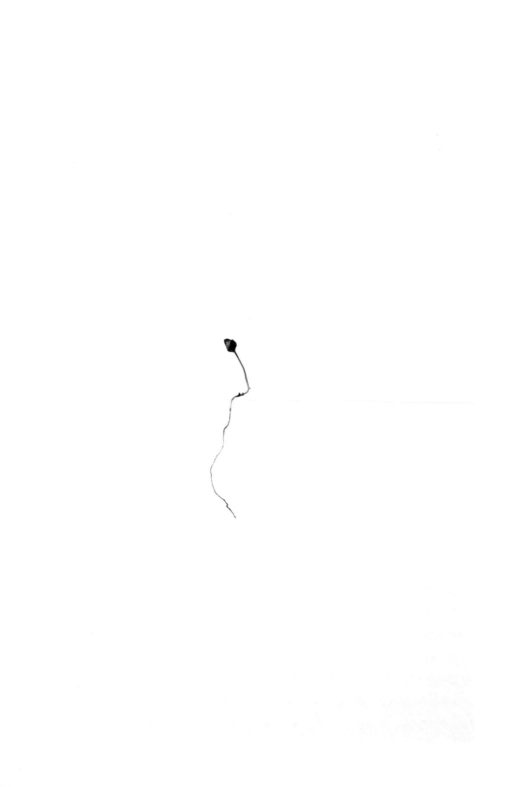

John Newling
Midlands, UK

14th January 2018

God
cc. Nature
The Earth

Dear God,

I have been writing to Nature.

Forgive my bluntness but do your teachings help us to form a relationship with Nature or are they simply about us?

I am perplexed with the sentiments of 'rule and subdue' that is talked of in your scripture; isn't this unhelpful?

Yours,
John

John Newling
Midlands, UK

Nature
The Earth

15th January 2018

Dear Nature,

I write to you on the understanding that I see you as a physical entity that causes and regulates phenomena in the world.

I am sure that, as a species, we want our culture to take the place of you; a desire for sovereignty over the world. To become the entity that causes and regulates phenomena in the world.

It is a sad truth that we have affected you; a tragic consequence of our desire.

It is even sadder if we think these effects give credence to our claim for sovereignty.

Sovereignty is our delusion. It is a delusion that threatens us and, as a consequence, many other living species.

We need to know that sovereignty is with you and will always be so.

Yours, with sorrow,
John

John Newling
Midlands, UK

Nature
The Earth

16th January 2018

Dear Nature,

We are leaving the European Union. This has made many people angry. Anger radicalises our thoughts and beliefs as the gap between the privileged rich and the forgotten poor becomes ever wider.

It seems that we are all retreating to our own frozen islands of belief; a place of comfort for some and dread for others. Do you have a view of sovereignty? The map on our kitchen wall defines borders of belonging, many of which are straight lines. I notice you have few straight lines in your ecology.

Yours, thinking the falcon cannot hear the falconer,
John

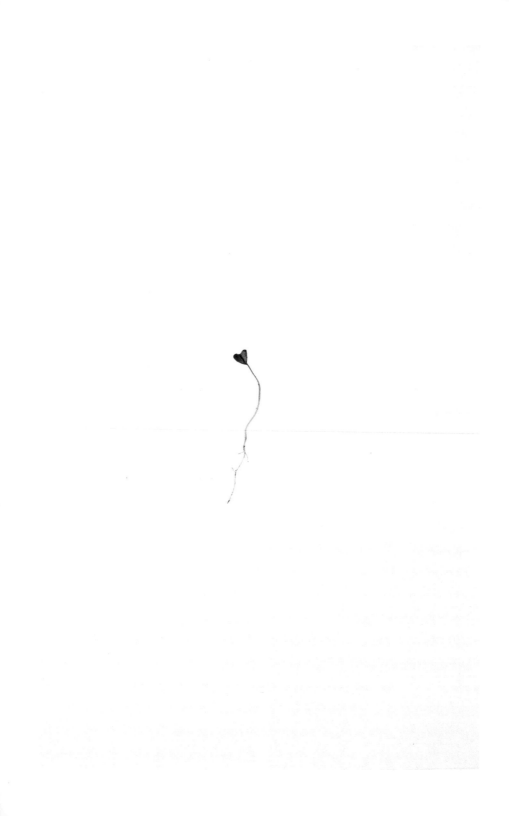

John Newling
Midlands, UK

17ᵗʰ January 2018

Nature
The Earth

Dear Nature,

I can imagine the sheer joy for the earliest of farmers as they produced food to feed themselves and their family. What a triumph of learning through you; a settled relationship.

But what happened when the farms produced a surplus? Surplus is a third party in our relationship; it is a place of separation. Surplus food gave the opportunity for trade or sales outside the needs of the community.

This is when we fell for the idea that you were, in some way, deficient.

Our need for a surplus focused attention on improving you; efficiency melded in the pressures of a market. We wanted more and more from you; growing yields belied the damage we were doing.

We signed our names in your soils.

Perhaps we did not know of this but we do now. It is a cycle that shows us our deficiencies. It is us that need to improve; we can do better.

No more signing in your soil.

Yours,
John

John Newling
Midlands, UK

Nature   18th January 2018
The Earth

Dear Nature,

Your soils have been drenched in chemicals and pounded by
machines year on year. Hedges have been removed and forests
cleared for land.

We now know this has and will drastically reduce your
fertility.

It is true that we have, in the pursuit of increasing yield for
food provision, damaged the diversity of life on the earth.

This is not to say that farmers are ignorant of our effects
on you, they are not. The problem is that they are caught
between earning a living and caring for the natural
environment.

We need to change this dangerous binary.

There are many good farmers.

We need to understand that values of care to the earth can be
seen as a commodity; essential and material. We can reward
the production of this commodity like any other.

We need food and we need care. If we are to survive we need
the two to be bound together forever.

Yours, with all manner of binding materials,
John

John Newling
Midlands, UK

19th January 2018

Farmers
cc. Nature
The Earth

Dear Farmers,

Please try to balance yield with care for the soil.
I know it is hugely complex.
I know you have to make a living.
I know you live in the uncertainty of a relationship
with nature.
I know it is a precarious balance.
I know sustainability is a challenge.
I know conservation may reduce yield.
I know reduced yield threatens an increase in the cost of food.
I know that, if we carry on as we are, our soils will lose
their fertility.
I know none of this is easy.
I know that between us all it has to be done.

Thank you.

Yours, with respect but worried,
John

John Newling
Midlands, UK

Nature
The Earth

20th January 2018

Dear Nature,

Last July I voted in a general election. It had been banging
on for seven weeks. During that time I can hardly recall
any mention of our relationship with you. You would have
thought we were neighbours on different continents.

I did wonder at the time how we can ever begin to understand
where we are. We need to look and think and wonder and
talk; but that seems to be less important than ensuring the
wealthy don't pay too much tax.

It's all 'mind the gap' or, more accurately, 'maintain the gap'.
Do you know of poverty? Does Nature have a working class?

Give me strength.

So much, to quote Keats, is nurtured by foppery and
barbarism.

Sorry.

Yours, finding it hard to avoid foppery and barbarism,
John

John Newling
Midlands, UK

Nature
The Earth

21st January 2018

Dear Nature,

Sometimes I wonder how I know I am here.

Yours,
John

John Newling
Midlands, UK

Nature
The Earth

22nd January 2018

Dear Nature,

We have ascribed many virtues to your trees. These are a mixture of material and mystical elements. From healing properties and physical characteristics, to trees of specific magic for ritual, and fruits that are bestowed with powers of longevity, trees have been given sacredness by succeeding generations of us.

Whilst many of these characteristics are entirely practical observations, strength and flexibility of the wood for example, many are wonderful imaginative connections between us and the trees.

These imagined associations are still with us. They evoke memories and senses that are as old as we are; each tree reminding us of a sublime language feeding our imaginative selves.

Thank you.

Yours,
John

John Newling
Midlands, UK

Nature   23rd January 2018
The Earth

Dear Nature,

Imagination is part of us.

I can imagine a tree running, a sun talking, a cow flying, a
soil laughing, a poppy weeping, a cloud shouting, a rhino
embroidering, a lawn listening, a river painting, a mountain
reading, a place I have never experienced.

Recently we have begun to realise that other species may also
be able to imagine. They may dream of places they have been.
Perhaps they envisage places they may not have experienced.

We know so little of you. I do know though, that our
imaginings will help mend our relationship.

Yours, walking in a dark forest of my imagination,
John

John Newling
Midlands, UK

Nature   24th January 2018
The Earth

Dear Nature,

Stories are very important to my species. We have stories read
to us as children. We learn to read. We read stories as adults.

Stories are wonderful things. They encourage our imagination.
They help us envisage things that are not given to us through
our senses. Imagination helps us learn.

Our stories of you are animated in ways we choose to
construct. Increasingly I have noticed children books that
imagine a better relationship between us and you.

Such stories playfully and imaginatively animate situations
between the young us and you.

I hope, as the young us grow up, we don't forget those early
stories.

Yours,
John

John Newling
Midlands, UK

Nature
The Earth

25th January 2018

Dear Nature,

One of the things I most like to do is change something into something else. Children do this all the time; a cardboard box becomes a place for treasures or a house or anything else that the imagination can conjure. I do wonder if that sense of transformation and play comes from our sense of you.

When we play our games of imagining transformations are we playing in parallel to you whose continual transformation constructs our environment? Is it your ecologies that work through our play?

Yours, forever playing,
John

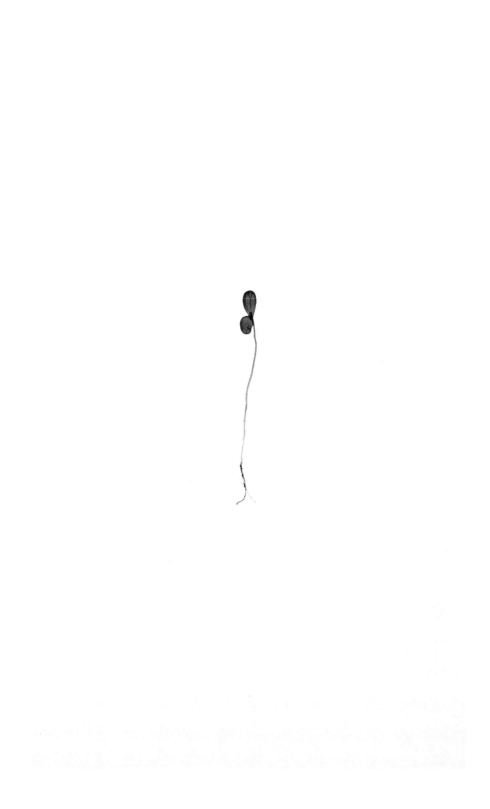

John Newling
Midlands, UK

Nature   26ᵗʰ January 2018
The Earth

Dear Nature,

The 21ˢᵗ December 2017 was the winter equinox. The
geometries between the lengths of day and night have been
touchstones for many generations. As a species we have
delineated meanings between shadows cast in sunlight and
those cast in moonlight.

One seems to be of growth and work, the other seems to be
of death and romance. In our 24/7 society I wonder if this
important sense of your geometries of light is somewhat
subdued. It was, and may continue to be, a time when an
astronomical phenomenon connects to our sense of you.

I guess we have built our own lights that dull the shadows of
the moon.

Yours,
John

John Newling
Midlands, UK

Nature
The Earth

27th January 2018

Dear Nature,

Ann came back from her last session studying John Milton's *Paradise Lost*. She had concluded that there can be no hope in heaven. This was an entirely logical conclusion from Milton's masterpiece. Heaven is a place where hope is not needed.

I was wondering if your complex ecology holds hope within it. I assume all living things in your domain must hope all the time; for food, shelter, weather and all that helps in survival. These are hopes that my species seems to share with you.

Do you ever hope my species would go away?

Yours,
John

John Newling
Midlands, UK

Nature   28th January 2018
The Earth

Dear Nature,

This winter Ann and I have been feeding birds with all kinds
of seeds and mixtures. We enjoy watching the birds feed and,
on occasion, the braver birds hop up the steps to our kitchen
door and peer at us peering at them. It is a strange kind of
communication lost somewhere in our ancient selves but it
does feel real.

I have noticed the blackbirds always eat the seeds on the
ground from the edge to the centre. My species learns from
such tiny observations. It is sad that we haven't understood
that we are a part of you and our learning tells us that if we
damage you it will hurt us. It is not a difficult proposition
after all.

Yours,
John

John Newling
Midlands, UK

Nature   29th January 2018
The Earth

Dear Nature,

There have been times when a phenomenon of yours takes my
breath away. I have responded by trying to take a photograph.
When I see the picture it is frequently disappointing as it
doesn't illustrate the visceral feeling I had whilst experiencing
the event.

We know, and recall, where we are because we experience a
variety of sensory information.

To focus on a single image impoverishes the recollection.
We lose other associations coalesced within our memory.

Lately I have observed people visiting a place often keep their
smartphone in their hand to take a picture of where they are.
These devices seem to hardly ever leave the eye as places are
captured and taken home.

I can't think that this helps us to remember where we
were, or are. If we recall experiences in the context of their
environments, then constantly taking pictures constricts our
memory of the place, event or phenomena.

We end up with a strangely glazed view of our environments
and the places within them.

We are in danger of forgetting that every place, event
and phenomena is held within an environment of you; a
dangerous amnesia.

Yours,
John

John Newling
Midlands, UK

30th January 2018

Nature
The Earth

Dear Nature,

I have been thinking about being in a place but not knowing where you are.

I walk a lot and enjoy just looking at where I am. I frequently see people taking pictures with their phones but I have become aware that they are reading from, or communicating through, smart phones. Their gaze seems to be at a fixed angle to the device, excluding what is around them. Undoubtedly these technologies are great tools for all of us but what environments are they creating?

As I walk it feels like other people are connected away from where they are.

Perhaps our technologies have created an environment where our cognition responds to this environment to the detriment of being in the physical environment. Trees are not seen, landscapes forgotten as we become immersed in other communities and social landscapes.

The danger of this is that it widens the gap between us and you.

If part of our evolution is adapting to changes in the environment then what does it mean to be living in a largely digital place. We can adapt more and more to this space but it may mean we forget to see and feel the place where we are.

I think we need to know where we are.

Yours, trying not to be lost,
John

John Newling
Midlands, UK

Nature   31st January 2018
The Earth

Dear Nature,

How do you share information?

Is information a part of your ecology?

As I watched the birds feeding I have recognised information
being shared accurately amongst the various species I have
observed. Is this specific only to the space outside our kitchen
door or does this learning spread to all similar situations?
I ask only because my species shares and replicates any
modification of behaviour rapidly and accurately. Ironically
this is why our technological and cultural endeavours are very
advanced. I say ironical because it is this very advance that
has shown to us our folly in the way we have treated you.

So, so sorry.

Yours,
John

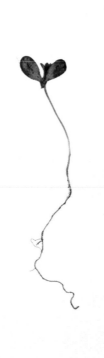

John Newling
Midlands, UK

Nature   1ˢᵗ February 2018
The Earth

Dear Nature,

I think it true that we need new, or newly remembered, values
within a shrinking set of values within our ecology.

Two places, the gallery and the garden, help me see
some possibilities.

The gallery and the garden are habits of learning. Each place
brings a sense of challenge and wonder. Each place helps
us see the world differently. Each place makes connections
between themselves and us. Each place shares its possibilities
as a social space.

Both places encourage us to understand our relationship with
our environments; both past, present and future.

The gallery and the garden are generous places. They connect
us to ourselves and to you. For me they are places where
newly remembered values are debated and evolved.

In our ecology of values they are environments that are
significant to many. As places of learning they should be at
the heart of all our curricula; schools for our common needs
to free our thinking and better connect with us and you.

I like galleries. I like gardens.

I hope you do too.

Yours,
John

John Newling
Midlands, UK

2ⁿᵈ February 2018

Nature
The Earth

Dear Nature,

A few summers back I watched a large vixen stalk, warily, into our garden. She was joined by a number of small cubs. She found herself a spot to lie down and began to feed her cubs.

This felt special to me. She seemed completely at ease lying in our garden. It felt like she knew she was safe in this place.

A year before this incident I had spent much of my time in the garden growing and making works from Jersey Kale 'walking stick cabbages'. It had been a project where I felt very connected to the space.

The fox incident was mesmerising and extraordinarily beautiful.

For months the vixen brought her cubs into the garden to play. Nearly every day that summer, in the last hours before dusk, the foxes arrived and played; completely joyous.

So it was that the play of foxes punctuated the liminal hours of our gaze.

This was a gift that connected us with you.

Yours, still loving watching our garden,
John

John Newling
Midlands, UK

Nature   3rd February 2018
The Earth

Dear Nature,

How do we learn about you? We are in and of you. You
teach us. We see them; we smell them; we hear them; we
touch them.

My species writes about you. From books on climatology
to guides on gardening, we are rapid to communicate your
complexity. Our libraries are full of works about you. As such,
we can respond to social and ecological changes through our
enormous cumulative culture.

I remember the first seeds I planted. I found the process of this
tiny seed becoming a plant entrancing. It helped me build a
relationship of sorts with you. I learnt a new language from
this and many other experiences of you.

It is learning that deepens our love.

Thank you.

Yours,
John

John Newling
Midlands, UK

Nature   4th February 2018
The Earth

Dear Nature,

Do you have a sense of value in all your complexity? We
humans use the word value a lot. Mostly we are referring to
the value of money. We exchange things for money. We are
enthusiastic for ownership of many things. We can own land.
We can buy and own a forest, or a mountain, or most things
in your dominion.

This is an individual ownership that can, and does, exclude
others. How strange.

I suppose there are similar territorial borders with other
species. It just feels like, with us, that we are in danger of not
seeing the woods for the money.

We have forgotten where we are.

Yours, not quite understanding the map,
John

John Newling
Midlands, UK

Land Owner
cc. Nature
The Earth

5th February 2018

Dear Land Owner,

I have recently been chatting to Nature.
I was wondering if you couldn't see the woods for the money.
Hope you can see the woods.

Yours,
John

John Newling
Midlands, UK

Nature
The Earth

6th February 2018

Dear Nature,

I live in a society that loves other animals and chooses to adopt some as pets. Mainly dogs and cats but many other species are brought into people's lives. It has been proven that a pet will give a sense of well-being. Pets are good for us.

I think we enjoy the sense of control and requited love that we perceive in these animals. I guess it's the simplicity of the relationship that delights us.

It is also a society that seems to love growing things in gardens and allotments. Maybe our loves of gardening and pet ownership are tiny ways of beginning to connect with you.

Both are relationships that remind us that we live with others within your realm.

Yours,
John

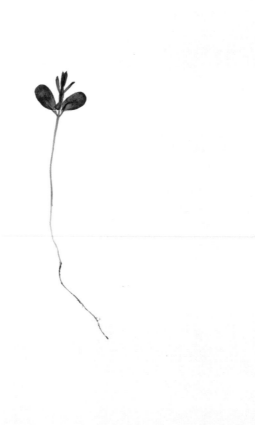

John Newling
Midlands, UK

Nature   7ᵗʰ February 2018
The Earth

Dear Nature,

Recently there has been a debate about sentience in other
species of animals. This has largely revolved around issues
of animal welfare. Sentience is deemed as necessary for the
ability to suffer. Those that suffer should be given rights.

By all accounts you have been suffering. Should you not be
given rights? Our ideas of your welfare are entirely for our
own good as a species. One day we will be able to prove that
you do experience our world subjectively.

When I walk in the environment I sense a vast intelligence
that spins around every step I might make. I cannot imagine a
non-sentient nature.

Sentience is also seen as a metaphysical quality of all things
that require respect and care. My species needs more than
ever to sense sentience in all living things. If we truly did that
we could change our world.

Yours, with care and respect,
John

John Newling
Midlands, UK

8th February 2018

Nature
The Earth

Dear Nature,

The Mayfly lives for twenty four hours. The Methuselah tree lives for up to five thousand years. We live for an average of seventy nine years.

Do you grieve loss?

I have read that many animals seem to sense death. Ann and I walked a dog called Rupert for a couple of years because our friend Bob was terminally ill. It was clear to us that their relationship was important to both Bob and Rupert. We noticed Rupert reacting to Bob's illness, especially during Bob's final months. Rupert became anxious to get back to Bob after a walk; he seemed depressed at times and definitely sensed Bob's illness.

What became apparent through our experience of watching the relationship with Bob and Rupert was that our human, subjective sense of living in the world was not exclusive to us. Other species share common feelings. I think we used to know this but have forgotten much of what we knew.

When we clear your land or radically change your habits I think you may grieve.

I am sorry.

Yours, lost in the cloud of unknowing,
John

John Newling
Midlands, UK

Nature
The Earth

9th February 2018

Dear Nature,

I have just been reading about the sixth mass extinction of animals. By many accounts we are in this new extinction phase now. Other species are becoming extinct a hundred times faster than they would without the impact of humans. Populations of wild animals have more than halved since 1970 while the human population has doubled.

This is a profoundly worrying sum.

We have done so much damage in ignorance but there is no excuse for our behaviour now; this is biological annihilation.

Words fail me.

Yours, dismayed by the arithmetic,
John

John Newling
Midlands, UK

Nature
The Earth

10th February 2018

Dear Nature,

In my society we have markets where goods of all kinds are exchanged for money. We also use the term to describe an area or space whereby people engage in exchange within a variety of systems, social relations, and institutions. Much is made of the choice available to us within these markets. The general sense is that the more choice for us in these markets the better.

This leads to huge amounts of stuff and services. The problem is that they are exchanged for differing amounts of money. Those with wealth have a much greater choice than others; choice is good for those that can choose.

We have a choice to respect and care about our relationship with you, regardless of privilege and monetary wealth.

Just saying.

Yours,
John

John Newling
Midlands, UK

Nature   11ᵗʰ February 2018
The Earth

Dear Nature,

When your forests are cleared, or your rivers dammed, or
your hedges cut, do you remember how they were?

I am always amazed by how quickly vegetation comes back
to those places. Are such sites of loss forever marked by
what was; a kind of natural cartography?

I would love to think that your memory holds and folds
your history of all places across all times. What a read that
would be.

Yours,
John

John Newling
Midlands, UK

Nature   12ᵗʰ February 2018
The Earth

Dear Nature,

I love digging your soil.
I love the smell, texture and colour of it.
I love what it is, what it sustains.

I have met experts on soil. They have told me of its incredible
complexity and beauty. They understand its structure through
astounding magnifications and rigorous analysis. They have
huge amounts of knowledge and apply this for the good of
everyone.

But despite, or maybe because of, their knowledge they also
say they love the smell, texture and colour of soil.

I find it encouraging that this is shared and common.

Yours,
John

John Newling
Midlands, UK

Plant Scientist   13th February 2018
cc. Nature
The Earth

Dear Plant Scientist,

Do you enjoy germinating and watching trees and plants grow?

I really hope you do.

Yours,
John

John Newling
Midlands, UK

Nature
The Earth

14th February 2018

Dear Nature,

My species has developed an economic system called capitalism. Capitalism is a system and ideology based upon private ownership of the means of production and their operation for profit. It is possibly the last of our ideologies that remains.

When your forests are cut down it is more often than not in order to capitalise on your space. The more I think about it the more I see that it is this pursuance of profit and subsequent wealth that has moved our gaze away from where we are. Such is the entrenchment of this system that many people think there is no alternative to it.

I am wondering if capitalism is a viral ideology embedded in the evolution of my species. I say this only because I think capitalism means that the pursuit of wealth and individual ownership has supplanted our pursuit of wellbeing and care for our environment.

Capitalism has shrunk the choice of values within our communities.

We are a clever and creative species and we can think with great imagination, but alternatives to capitalism are seen to be beyond us. They don't need to be. We could learn from you.

What a mess. What to do?

Yours,
John

John Newling
Midlands, UK

Nature
The Earth

15th February 2018

Dear Nature,

I am sure we need a new way of acknowledging what
are essential needs between us and essential values in our
relationship with you.

The problem with our current system of currency and
rewards is that it is unable to extract itself from larger global
systems of capital. Currently money is a token or a promise
that is subject to an old system of industrialised production
and consumption. The connection between currency and
global profit does not allow for money to be given against
the production say, of a better soil or cleaner air or a better
community.

I am not an economist but I sense that, if we can develop a
system that rewards actions and works that are of greater
value to all people then we may be able to unblock the
debilitating model where profit and yield cannot be separated
and are subject to an outmoded singular economic model.

I think we could develop micro-economies of value that
may help us begin to revalue our relationship with you and
between ourselves. These independent tokens may allow our
ecology of values to emerge in a way that helps us and you.

Our future may depend on small, independent, and localised
economies based on ecologies of value for the many.

Yours, sensing we need a new economic model,
John

John Newling
Midlands, UK

Nature
The Earth

16th February 2018

Dear Nature,

Wealth creation is a good thing. It gives us an opportunity
to share the wealth. Our problem is that the distribution of
wealth has become increasingly poor. We have forgotten to
share with others. The gaps between poor and wealthy have
been so vast that our species may feel that its constituent
groups live on different planets.

Sharing is at the core of making us a social group of animals;
it helps us learn and grow as a species. The need to share has
been in us for thousands of years. Sharing connects us.

Income brings opportunities. Opportunities are what all
people of the world need.

It has been suggested that giving everyone an unconditional,
universal, income would be a way of beginning to narrow the
gaps between our wealth and consequent opportunities.

Studies have shown that an unconditional income will
encourage people to create more possibilities. This would help
in our welfare; we all need to be needed for something.

In forgetting to share our wealth we may also have forgotten
that your distribution shares all with all.

I hope yours can be the example to us.

Yours, hoping we wake up and smell the poverty,
John

John Newling
Midlands, UK

Nature   17th February 2018
The Earth

Dear Nature,

I have just walked into a tree.

I cut my forehead quite badly. I had been thinking about
these letters.

I laughed; I hope you did too.

Yours, bloodied and laughing,
John

John Newling
Midlands, UK

Nature   18th February 2018
The Earth

Dear Nature,

You are probably getting fed up with all this mail.

I think I write them to clarify my thoughts; to try to
understand my relationship within you.

We have had a shrinking ecology of values. Money is
embedded in our private, singular, worlds as the core
aspirant, a measure of survival. Meshing this value with our
evolutionary traits has been a disaster for our relationship
within you.

I think I can say that the terrible gap between us and you
is beginning to shrink as more and more of us do try to
understand the importance of you.

But it remains a precarious balance.

Yours,
John

John Newling
Midlands, UK

19th February 2018

Nature
The Earth

Dear Nature,

As part of my work I have grown many plants and trees.
Each one has given me a great sense of a co-relationship
between it and me. The slow time observation of these growing
forms teaches me much and focuses my sense of where I am.

I greatly enjoy the geometry of the growth of each plant or tree.
Each form twists and spins with the actions of soil and sun.

On a winter's day I can just stand under a tree and feel the spin.

On a spring day I can just stand under a tree and feel its pulse.

On a summer's day I can just stand under the tree and feel the
energy being released.

On an autumn day I can just stand under a tree and feel the
slow slide to sleep.

Your spin, pulse, energy and sleep are shared in us.

Thank you.

Yours,
John

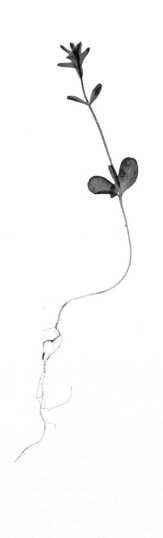

John Newling
Midlands, UK

Nature
The Earth

20th February 2018

Dear Nature,

Why do I like gardening so much?

Is it the fresh air? Is it seeing plants growing? Is it watching
how the sun moves across the garden? Is it the sense of slow
time? Is it being able to know where and when is best to plant
seeds? Is it watching squirrels, foxes, and birds using the same
space as a place? Is it imagining the language between species?
Is it touching, smelling and digging soil? Is it watering the
garden? Is it cutting the grass? Is it sensing a mysterious and
unknown language beneath our feet? Is it looking closely?
Is it that it makes me feel and think better? Is it some sense
of a co-relationship of care? Is it feeling in some small way
connected?

I really don't know, but I do enjoy it.

Yours,
John

John Newling
Midlands, UK

Head Gardener
cc. Nature
The Earth

21st February 2018

Dear Head Gardener,

You once told me that weeds do not have Latin names – I'm not sure this is true. I guess some of our gardens have the class of classification at work.

Strange that we view weeds as something undesirable. They are wild plants. True, they grow where they are not wanted and compete with cultivated plants. Good for them.

In a society that adheres to the cultivated in most things, weeds seem to me to be the mavericks of our gardens.

I like weeds.

Come on the weeds.

Yours,
John

John Newling
Midlands, UK

Common Gardener
cc. Nature
The Earth

22nd February 2018

Dear Common Gardener,

I have been writing to Nature.

Thank you for all your digging and bending and planting
and thinking.

As you rub in the Ralgex and sweep the dirt from the kitchen
floor, remember the folds of soil on your spade. They are the
folds of another language given freely for us to learn.

Keep digging, keep learning.

Yours,
John

John Newling
Midlands, UK

Nature   23rd February 2018
The Earth

Dear Nature,

We enjoy patterns. Humans of all ages love drawing patterns.
Some patterns are repeated across cultures and are, sometimes,
seen as codes for being in the world. They are a kind of
language. When these patterns become uncertain we experience
moments of stress, fear, frustration and, sometimes, anger.

It is no different when your patterns appear to be inconsistent
with our assumptions. When spring is late, or winter seems to go
on and on, or summer brings rain and cloud, we feel the impact.

In an atavistic response some of us will feel the unpredictable
weather is associated with something we may have done.
Our distant ancestors knew of this.

Often these irregular patterns are viewed as your inconstancy;
climate seen as something forever other. In our frustration we
blame you; we think we can't change the weather.

But we have.

Acknowledging that we have an impact on your patterns is not
new. We forgot this as rationalism superseded our subjectivity.
Our contemporary selves can now see rational evidence for our
impact; we are coming full circle in our relationship with you.

With impact comes responsibility.

Yours, hoping for a greater responsibility from all of us,
John

John Newling
Midlands, UK

Nature   24th February 2018
The Earth

Dear Nature,

I have been looking at other words commonly associated
with you. 'Outside' is one of the most common.

This word does point to you being seen as aside or outside of
us. The anthropological technique of participant observation
is a method I am aware of in my own work. It suggests being
at the edge of things, whilst simultaneously being in the
centre.

I think in our relationship with you, we have moved away
from participant to observer. If we become non-participant
observers in our relationship to you, we become strangers so
to speak. Further, we become strangers without a stake in the
relationship. Perhaps this has happened.

Recently I came across the phrase 'to have skin in the game'.
As I understand this, it means to have incurred risk by being
involved in achieving a goal. We need to have skin in the
game of better understanding our relationship with you.

More skin, more participation.

Yours,
John

John Newling
Midlands, UK

Paul Crutzen
cc. Nature
The Earth

25th February 2018

Dear Paul Crutzen,

I have been writing to Nature.

Thank you for using the term Anthropocene as a geological period denoting significant human impact on the Earth's geology and ecosystems. In naming this epoch you gave identity to our impact.

I hope and believe that your naming of this geological period has brought more skin into the game with regard to our relationship with nature. We are now participants in this relationship.

Your word has stopped us being strangers.

Yours,
John

John Newling
Midlands, UK

Nature
The Earth

26th February 2018

Dear Nature,

A common phrase used by us is 'getting on in life'.

We like the weather to be determined, by and large, by seasonal changes. We want a sense of a predetermined rhythm to our climate.

Through our actions we have increased levels of carbon dioxide in our atmosphere; in doing so we have affected the effects of natural phenomena. These changes impact on us all and require that people take action.

In our relationship with you we seem to have perpetuated a double bind. On one hand we need to better care for the environment, on the other that care means we have to radically change our values. Our 'getting on in life' becomes a conflicted message.

This condition of social, economic and cultural schizophrenia requires us to radically re-think how we are in the world in relation to you. If we don't, I fear it will not end well.

We need to move from 'getting on in life' to 'getting on with life' where life refers to you.

Yours, trying to get on with life,
John

John Newling
Midlands, UK

27th February 2018

Nature
The Earth

Dear Nature,

I have been thinking about time recently; particularly in regard to our relationship with you.

When we re-enact an event from our history we are performing it outside the context of time.

A renewed consciousness of you has generated a desire for a closer connection. The relationship has been associated with a spectrum of benefits from wellbeing to the survival of our species.

When we grow foods in our allotments or forage in your landscapes or dig the earth in our gardens are we re-enacting our perceived relationship to you?

I am not so sure. I think our relationship to you may alter in emphasis at times but, by and large, I think we still share the fears and desires of our hunters, gatherers and farmers in relation to you. These genetic ghosts may change the emphasis of our relationship but they are touchstones in that relationship.

I see activities like foraging, gardening, tending allotments as initiation dances in our relationship to you.

I think the problem is we have forgotten to dance but are perhaps, beginning to remember.

Yours, dancing in many places,
John

John Newling
Midlands, UK

Nature
The Earth

28th February 2018

Dear Nature,

Like many people, Ann and I enjoy picking blackberries.
Every year we go to a place we know that has an abundance
of these fruits. Foraging has become more and more popular
in our society. It seems to be a behaviour that fills a need.

Maybe it is an echo of our hunting and gathering ways when
we primarily depended on wild food to survive. Maybe it's a
need to pick food directly from a place we have discovered
for ourselves. Maybe it's a need to experience eating foods
at source. Maybe it's because the food eaten is free of our
associations with cost; strangely liberating. Maybe it's because
we are so used to thinking of a nature that is owned that we
see foraging as an act of defiance; a kind of natural theft.

It is a theft that shows just how far away from you we have
grown. We see you as not of us.

Our blood-red blackberry stained hands are signs of what we
were; we enjoy re-enacting our behavioural ecology.

These may be rehearsals of what we once were but what we
were is what we are now. Much has changed but our essential
selves need to connect to you.

Yours, rehearsing in the now,
John

John Newling
Midlands, UK

Nature
The Earth

1st March 2018

Dear Nature,

Love is a word often used by my species. It is word that advocates absolute trust in a relationship. You can love something but that love may not be reciprocated. Love is commonly viewed as an emotion; an intense feeling of deep affection for someone.

Whilst it may be an emotion, I think it is principally a state of mind associated with actions in relation to our being in the world and being in the world with others. It is an enacted emotion of great importance to us. It is, perhaps, our greatest achievement.

It may be we give the word significance because it requires trust and we find trusting anything so very difficult. We struggle to trust each other. To act lovingly is not as easy as it may seem. When something or someone we have trusted confounds that trust it can be devastating to us; things fall apart.

Imagine if your spring didn't come or your rains did not arrive, our trust and, maybe, our love for you turns into an anger brought on by fear. This is no excuse for our behaviour towards you but it is a kind of sad truth.

We want to trust you but forget that means trusting ourselves; we are part of you.

Yours,
John

John Newling
Midlands, UK

Nature   2nd March 2018
The Earth

Dear Nature,

I have been thinking more about love and you.

Your regulation of phenomena means energy cannot be
destroyed but can only be transformed from one form to
another. Yours is the regulation of all that was and all that
becomes.

We are one of those energies.

Much as we seem to think we are a separate entity outside of
your regulation we are not.

We may destroy ourselves but that energy will be transformed
in form.

I find a strange comfort in that thought.

Yours, less scared,
John

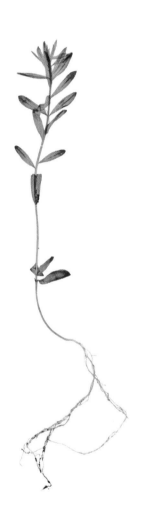

John Newling
Midlands, UK

Nature
The Earth

3rd March 2018

Dear Nature,

I have heard the government are planning to create a database on how much money a student earns after completing a degree. Each course subject within each university will be part of this list. It will be a ranking of subjects studied in terms of future wealth.

I assume the government believes such a list will inform the choices for new applicants.

We seem to want or need to monetise everything. Monetary value has subverted our own understanding of our needs and desires that were once not associated with such a value.

Monetary exchange and transactions have become the dominant institution that folds all subjects into it, tending to give value only to its significance as a market.

The value of subject knowledge becomes increasingly lost.

Learning, with its acquisition of knowledge, is one of our great assets and joys as a species. To narrow the value of such learning to the value of wealth generation alone is utterly sad; a terrible mistake.

Value needs to liberate itself from money.

Yours, feeling a bit grumpy,
John

John Newling
Midlands, UK

Nature   4th March 2018
The Earth

Dear Nature,

Our garden has large hedges along its borders. The hedge is
the habitat for many birds, and other animals. In the evening
I often watch families of birds going in and out of our hedge;
a joy to watch.

Hedges are important. They support large percentages of our
woodland birds, mammals, butterflies and frogs, newts and
other species.

It is estimated that in a six year period between 1984 and 1990
hedgerow length in England declined by almost a quarter.
This accounted for the removal of 5,903 miles of hedge each
year.

Over the six years that is a distance of 35,418 miles of habitat.
That's a very, very long hedge and a terrible loss of habitat.

We need to plant more hedges.

Yours,
John

John Newling
Midlands, UK

Farmers
cc. Nature
The Earth

Dear farmers everywhere,

Please plant more hedges.
Proszę posadź więcej żywopłotów.
S'il vous plaît planter plus de haies.
Por favor planta más setos.
Bitte pflanzen Sie mehr Hecken.
Si prega di piantare più siepi.
Vänligen plantera fler häckar.
Пожалуйста, посадите больше кустов.

Thank you.

Yours,
John

John Newling
Midlands, UK

6th March 2018

Nature
The Earth

Dear Nature,

You have areas within your domain that are uncultivated and
uninhabited by us. We call these wildernesses or wild land.
These are places where we can experience you without the
signs of us.

I have stood in uninhabited land and reflected on what it is to
be human.

I have stood looking out to sea and reflected on what it is to
be human.

Visiting the wild lands and wild seas prompt reflections on our
relationships with you and others. It takes us into a temporal
zone where your slow time merges, momentarily, within us.

These moments are important to our ecology of values.
Our ecology of values is important to our relationship with
you. We lose these moments at great expense to us and to you.

We have destroyed a tenth of your remaining wilderness in the
last twenty five years. There may be none left within a century.

Yours, lost for words once more,
John

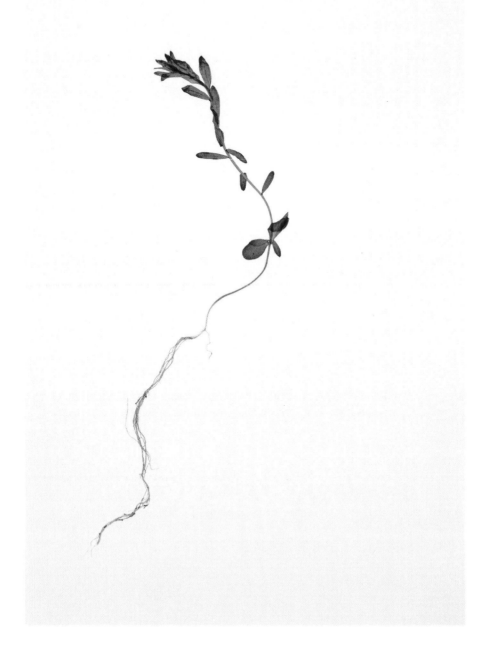

John Newling
Midlands, UK

Nature
The Earth

7th March 2018

Dear Nature,

Sometimes I think I only know that I am here when I become
estranged from here.

Yours, saddened, scared and scarred,
John

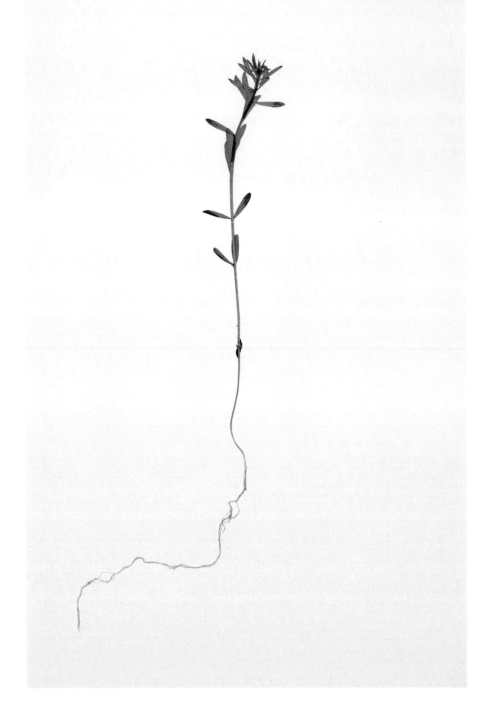

John Newling
Midlands, UK

Nature   8th March 2018
The Earth

Dear Nature,

The weight of the earth has changed relatively little
throughout its existence. In the first law of conservation the
mass of the earth is constant in spite of physical or chemical
changes that may happen. In the second law of conservation
energy cannot be created or destroyed.

It is estimated that forty-thousand tonnes of dust a year from
our solar system becomes part of the matter of our Earth.

Everything on Earth is formed of the dust that was produced
by unimaginable events in our solar system. You and I share
the same matter.

Mass is constant and energy cannot be destroyed.

Perhaps we need a third law of conservation; humans can
be changed by environments that have been destroyed by
other humans.

Has to be said.

Yours,
John

John Newling
Midlands, UK

9th March 2018

Nature
The Earth

Dear Nature,

It is estimated that 100.5 billion of us have died on your earth.

That's a lot of ghosts in your soils.

Sometimes my shadow alone touches you. The rest of me is
lost somewhere else.

Trying to find where here is.
Trying to find what here is.
Trying to find why here is.

There're a lot of ghosts in your soils.

Yours,
John

John Newling
Midlands, UK

Nature   10th March 2018
The Earth

Dear Nature,

In your biosphere all matter is recycled as a basis for the elemental cycles in our ecosystems. Energy flows, moving from concentrated forms to more dissipated forms.

We are here.

Perhaps we don't know where we are because we want to be somewhere else. Our restless selves have conjured many special places that are exclusive to us and outside of you.

The problem is that these great manifestations of our imaginative longings for our own islands of paradise take our attention away from where we are. Such islands have created some of our greatest cultural works in our history; it would be silly to not value them. They are our sense of our spiritual selves made evident in the most beautiful ways.

It is just that I sense that if we spent more time being where we are, we would understand it as the most extraordinary, beautiful and sublime place. Being where we are generates great cultural works of our spiritual selves in and of this place.

It may be in our nature to look elsewhere but that very nature can make us lost in our relationship to you.

Yours, trying to be here,
John

John Newling
Midlands, UK

Nature
The Earth
11th March 2018

Dear Nature,

Just been watching the refuse collectors pick up our rubbish
for recycling.

Watching them I was reminded of you.

A weekly ritual that felt like a small act in an elemental cycle;
all matter is recycled.

Thanks bin men and bin women.

Yours,
John

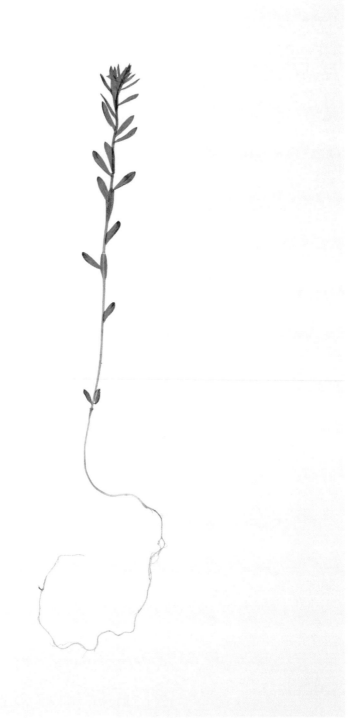

John Newling
Midlands, UK

Nature   12th March 2018
The Earth

Dear Nature,

This morning I listened to a short news item about your seas
and oceans. The report made it clear that we know very little
about the beds of your oceans and seas.

We love finding out about unknowns and bring wonderful
knowledge to the world. I was excited to hear this. As a
species we need to explore and exploring your mysteries is
another way of us connecting.

But then the review highlighted the fact that we could exploit
the oceans and seas for mineral, oils, gas and anything new
we discover in the future. It was that word exploit that made
my heart sink. It is no different from the word subdue found
in Genesis.

Why does everything we find out about have to be exploited?
Can we really exploit sustainably? Can we really subdue
sustainably?

I can see a time when the beds of your seas and oceans are
crisscrossed with the borders of countries claiming ownership;
another sad map of sovereignty.

We have signed in your soils and now we will sign in your
oceans beds; such a terrible conceit.

What to do?

Yours, feeling estranged and ashamed once more,
John

John Newling
Midlands, UK

Nature
The Earth

Dear Nature,

We are not neighbours.
We do not visit you.
We are not separate from you.
We are not elsewhere.
We are here.

Please help us understand this.

Yours, without maps,
John

John Newling
Midlands, UK

Nature
The Earth

Dear Nature,

The sun is shining this morning.

It has been a dark and long winter. When the sun shines we seem to feel better in the world.

You store sunlight as chemical energy, in all your organic compounds. That includes us.

Light is at the heart of many of our rituals, beliefs and narratives. Its presence and absence has flowed through our stories across the myriad of spoken languages.

Many of our stories connect us to you as poetic renditions of our experiences of you. They have been passed down the generations in oral and written traditions.

Many of these works do have in them our struggle to form our relationship with you.

Perhaps it has always been a struggle for us. Light and its absence remain the common metaphor of the good and bad of our behaviour. Many of our stories tell us of our moral connections with you; both as warnings and ethical measures.

The sun is shining this morning.

Yours, with more energy,
John

John Newling
Midlands, UK

Nature
The Earth

15th March 2018

Dear Nature,

As antidotes to our mortality we often imagine our longings
into places.

Entry to these places of eternity is often granted or denied as
a judgement on our behaviour in life.

We conflate our death with access to spaces we have
constructed; each space bringing joy or pain depending on the
bouncers at their gates.

It can be argued that such places encourage good behaviour
or discourage bad behaviour in the lives we live. We are
social animals. I think we want to live good lives. Our need
to be needed is part of that behaviour and is adopted by the
many. Better to be a good person in the here and now in the
knowledge that our deaths are part of an incredible system of
us within you.

When we die our matter is recycled and our energy flows: a
slow and widening river across the biosphere; what a place to
be in and part of forever. Our energy swallowed in the breath
of another animal or gathered in the leaves of trees or rain
from a cloud or floating on the oceans floor.

An eternity in a place of great wonder: a paradise of sorts.

Not sure about bouncers.

Yours,
John

John Newling
Midlands, UK

16th March 2018

Nature
The Earth

Dear Nature,

I am sure many of my species have stood and looked at your landscapes and breathed deeply, reflecting on beauty. Such slow, quiet moments are a vital principle in our wellbeing. Some would call this a spiritual rite.

Spirituality is necessarily ambiguous. The ambiguity allows a freedom for all in what they sense as spiritual. For many, gazing at your landscapes and experiencing your phenomena are acts of sacred reflection. We can feel tiny within the world whilst, simultaneously, feeling a vital connection to it. We sense that we are needed in that connection.

Being needed for something is important for all of us. We express this necessity in many parts of our lives. In truth we know you do not need us; but we do need you. Whilst what we have done to you is terrible, it may be that in our struggle to try to co-exist with you we find that need.

We are at least talking.

Yours,
John

John Newling
Midlands, UK

17th March 2018

Nature
The Earth

Dear Nature,

Spring has begun to stutter into our garden.

Life emerging from your soils and gathering on your trees is a force that we all feel.

Soon the trees will be covered in their blossoms, ticked on in your time.

We long for this.

A strange relief comes to us. It is happening again, and again is a word we hold dear.

Repeated and repeated your clock is our most loved measure of where we may be.

Rituals, of old and of now, play in us ticking in your time.

Spring has begun to stutter into our garden and it makes us feel better.

Yours,
John

John Newling
Midlands, UK

Nature   18th March 2018
The Earth

Dear Nature,

Things are looking up. There are many conservation
projects around the world that are trying to restore habitats.
People are beginning to be more conscious of you and our
relationship to you.

This could be seen as restorative justice as we begin to
try to undo some of what we have done. Restoration and
conservation are twin actions that meld our ecologies in a
possible symbiosis. It is hugely paradoxical that we cause a
change in your climate, show evidence of ourselves in your
soil and are instrumental in a mass extinction of other species
and then create a perception that we are needed as we try to
put our mistakes right.

But now is a time for pragmatism as we restore and conserve
places that are you.

It may just be a pragmatism that changes our sense of both us
and you.

Yours, hopefully,
John

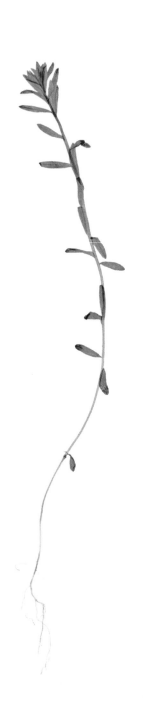

John Newling
Midlands, UK

Nature
The Earth

19th March 2018

Dear Nature,

In our kitchen we have a map of the world and a map of the UK.

Maps are beautiful things but I have always felt wary of them.

I think this is because they present us with a world delineated in exquisite detail whilst being a reminder of how we have subdued the earth.

I have had a constant tick in the back of my mind that a map is not the territory.

Yours is the territory.

Knowing where we are is complicated.

Yours, trying to be where I am,
John

John Newling
Midlands, UK

Nature   20th March 2018
The Earth

Dear Nature,

It has been snowing. I watched the landscape out of my
window slowly being blanketed in a whiteness that muffles
all it falls on. It was a beautiful picture.

I had to leave this view to get some food. It was cold, with a
ferocious wind and I struggled to walk to my local shop and
back. It was a very different experience to watching the flakes
of falling snow earlier. It felt physical and real and I was
happy to have walked in it.

There has been a large rise in technologies that mediate our
experience of you. Digital augmentations and simulations of
you are very popular.

My worry is that these technological natures are entirely
controlled by us. This may be the nature we have always
wanted but my emotional need for you include the challenges,
unpredictability and wildness of you. I do not want to
experience you only through glass.

I want to live in your risks and dangers.

Yours, viscerally,
John

John Newling
Midlands, UK

Nature
The Earth

21st March 2018

Dear Nature,

We have changed the climate.
We are under the weather.

We have changed our climate.
We are under our weather.

Yours,
John

John Newling
Midlands, UK

Nature
The Earth

22nd March 2018

Dear Nature,

I have been thinking about your language.

It seems to be of decay and death and growth and renewal
and light and dark and heat and cold and wind and birds and
earth and mud and fields and hills and seas and rivers and
mountains and colours and plants and trees and hedges and
skies and ice and roots and leaves and whirlwinds and cows
and monkeys and gold and emeralds and so much more.

It is a language in which I have yet to become fluent, but I
am trying.

Yours,
John

John Newling
Midlands, UK

Nature   23ʳᵈ March 2018
The Earth

Dear Nature,

My species has always mimicked aspects of you; notably
rituals where the wearing of costumes or the actual skins of
other animals are performed. This is an old need to try and
possess the attributes of other species; mimicking to inhabit
that species and transfer their characteristics to us.

We mimic to transfer attributes.

Now we are learning to mimic your ecological wonders.
Biomimicry applies what we learn from close observations of
you to our built environments.

It is a transfer that connects your attributes to us. At the very
least it is an acknowledgement that we can learn from you.

Yours,
John

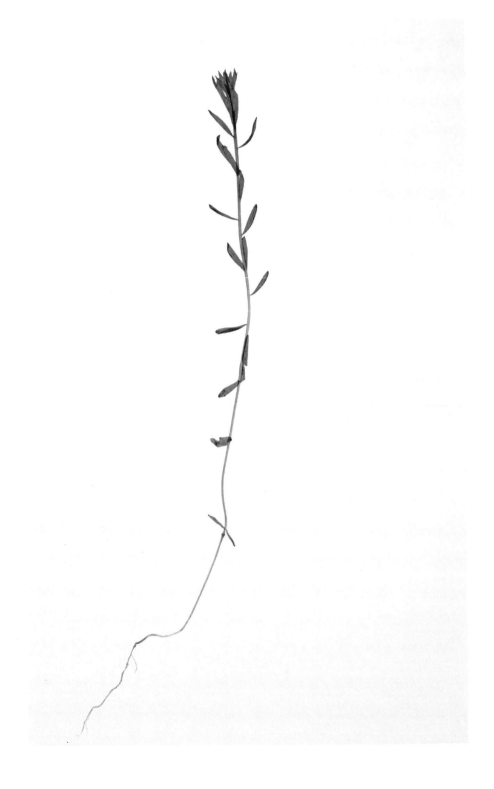

John Newling
Midlands, UK

Nature
The Earth

24th March 2018

Dear Nature,

People are using less water in their baths.
People are travelling more on public transport.
People are recycling more things.
People are planting trees.
People are restoring habitats.
People are clearing rubbish from their environment.
People are reducing their carbon footprints.
People are trying to live sustainably.

It is the accumulative actions, however small, of people that
will change our relationship with you.

Small solidarities from us.

Yours, a person,
John

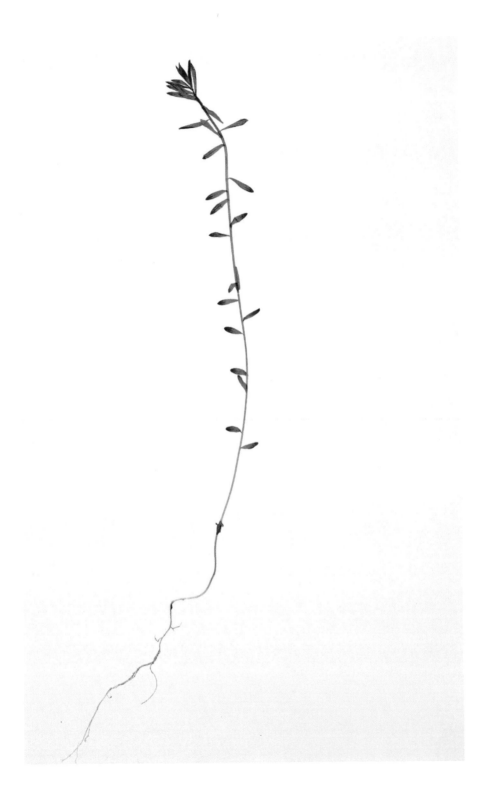

John Newling
Midlands, UK

Nature   25th March 2018
The Earth

Dear Nature,

In all evolution adaptive traits are functional, evolved through
natural selection. Each trait is understood as causing fitness
to increase, where the genes of future generations are better
adapted to their environment.

I think that, given that you are our environment, our species
should evolve traits that adapt to you.

This may already be happening as we see the effects of our
actions. We have the knowledge to understand the risks to
our future generations.

This could be good news as we struggle to read our
relationship to you. Adaptive traits may be the restorative
justice you need.

I don't know how many generations of us it will take for
these traits to be adopted in our genes but my heart felt hope
is that we will evolve them as matter of our survival.

Yours,
John

John Newling
Midlands, UK

Nature
The Earth

26th March 2018

Dear Nature,

What to do?

We need a revolution in our behaviours and attitudes towards you.

We need to care and bring restorative justice to you.

We need to make clear, through education, social interactions, global trade and many other agencies that we are living with you and have a stake in your welfare.

We need to understand that being in you with all our senses is better than an augmented version of you.

We need to develop our technologies to help meet these needs.

We need to be needed and remember where we are.

We need to understand that, in our ecology of values, our actions towards you are fundamental.

We need to know your welfare is our welfare.

Yours, with hope,
John

John Newling
Midlands, UK

Nature
The Earth

27th March 2018

Dear Nature,

A lament.

> We were lovers; your unknowns folded
> us in fear and wonder.
>
> We signed our names in your soils lost
> in our clearing and clearings.
>
> Our shadows alone touched you trying
> to find where here is.
>
> Wanting here to be elsewhere we became
> estranged.

I am sorry but, perhaps, we are moving towards knowing
what here means.

Yours,
John

John Newling
Midlands, UK

28th March 2018

Nature
The Earth

Dear Nature,

Our stardust selves are restless. We are keen to move.
When our moving vans become rockets we will be swapping
biospheres.

Several science and space exploration laboratories are
working on growing plants in differing habitats. We have
learnt much about plant behaviours from your ecology.
We want to mimic such behaviour in other atmospheres.

From moon plants to lunar greenhouses we are going to take
our gardens to other planets. In so doing we are echoing your
biological systems in the process of settling in a new habitat.

Whether we settle on a new planet as a necessity of survival or
to test possibilities it will be the knowledge you have given us
that we take with us. Thank you.

On the side of each rocket, emblazoned in bold letters are the
words: *Don't Do That Again.*

We need to remember.

Yours,
John

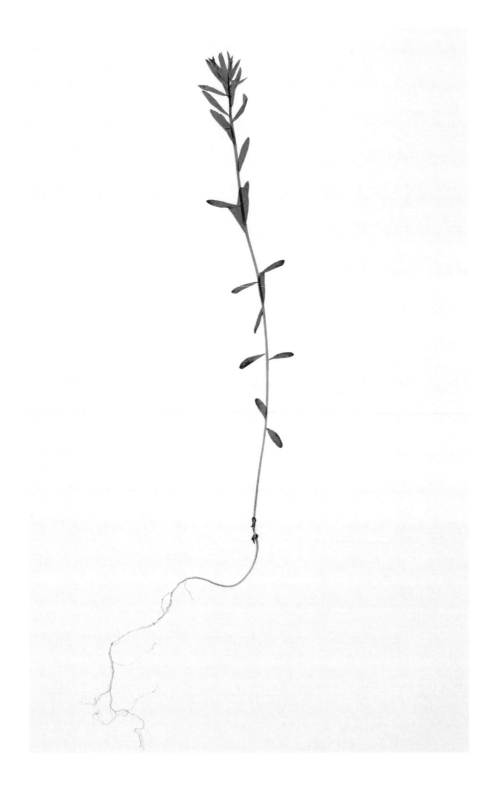

John Newling
Midlands, UK

29th March 2018

Nature
The Earth

Dear Nature,

I love the unknowns of you.

Yours,
John

Afterword

John Newling
Midlands, UK

A Reader
The Earth

3rd August 2020

Dear Reader,

It has been 859 days since I completed the 81st, and last, letter to Nature. The 81 days preceding that had been intense and all-consuming.

I needed to write these letters for many reasons. Sometimes my thoughts become so cramped that I have to release them and the letters were a means of this release; an exhaled breath of histories, reconciliations, possibilities and wonder that had built up in me. For a while it seemed like so many bad signs were falling into each other, building an aggregate of uncertainty and urgency. Like many, I felt a strange kind of helplessness. All in all, with the exception of a handful of people I love, I began to fall out with my own species; not a good thing.

Mumbling, pleading and occasionally roaring through my thoughts was the largest of elephants in the room; climate change. This elephant cast a gloomy shadow of our dysfunctional relationship with the earth that we live on.

The antidote was to explore where I am. My neighbourhood, our garden and local parks were places and spaces that nourished my sense of the truly wonderful and mysterious nature of the earth with its systems of balance and connectedness. This was not new to me, trying to find where I am and how I connect to it has been an exploration for as long as I can remember. Nevertheless, the gloomy shadow stayed with me. I needed to find a way to express my thoughts; to cast more light into the room, to lighten the shadow.

And so, on 8th January 2018, I found myself sitting at a keyboard and typing a letter to Nature. As with many of my works, at the start, I had no idea where this simple act would lead. Every morning I would wake thinking about the day's letter and, later, fall into dreams with further thoughts about tomorrow's letter. As the text grew and evolved I found I was beginning to articulate doubts and possibilities that may help us to better connect to where we live. It was a cathartic mapping of my thoughts and a seeding of ideas.

This is not an academic text, it is a deeply personal account; crafted as a text of reconciliation, truth and hope. It holds human frailties, occasional contradictions, and the struggle for the right word. It became an honest attempt to construct a work that reflects where we are and where we could go.

Right now, we are living through a global pandemic. It has been terrible and sad; many people are grieving. Yet in May this year, we witnessed the most wonderful spring I can remember. This was nature full-on with an awakening that seemed at its most intense. So much growth, long hours of sunshine, quiet roads and cleaner air. It felt like nature was trying to talk to us. Some of the acts of kindness I saw on daily lockdown walks were joyous and showed what, as species, we can be. Local communities came into their own and took responsibility for where they were. Our streets became ours as cars sat unmoving and silent. I do hope we can remember these positive experiences and learn from them.

Another consideration was the book itself. When I was writing the letters I was also growing flax from seed in our garden. This was connected to a residency I was doing in France. Alongside each letter is a pressed flax seedling, spanning the days of the early growth of the beautiful plant. By flicking the pages it is possible to animate this growth; a dance that is near my heart.

The letters begin with "I have always loved the unknowns of you but can we ever truly be together?" and end with "I love the unknowns of you". In between, the Dear Nature letters fold thoughts, hopes, desires, frustrations, aspirations and histories into themselves.

It is a thread of thoughts, a correspondence with an old friend who answers in languages that I want to learn; languages that are fluent in all manner of life.

This is the second edition of this work. Robert Frost said, "I have miles to go before I sleep"; I hope we do, I have many more letters to come.

Thank you.

Love and good health,

John

Flax (Linum usitatissimum)
The images in this book record the growth of a flax plant. The seeds were given to me by Franck Sagaert, a flax farmer from Dieppe, in relation with my Dieppe-Haven residency.

Acknowledgements

With special thanks to
Sarah Shalgosky, curator, University of Warwick Art Collection
Liz Dooley, deputy curator, University of Warwick Art Collection
Ann Newling

Thanks to the supporters of this edition

Chris Arden Jones
Alice Bird
Cole Buxton
Pamela Davis
Fiona Day
Mark Hope
Derek Horton

Janice Howard
Henrietta Inman
Al Kennedy
David Keyte
Mark Leahy
Fenella Mett
David Newport

Lisa Osborn
Christopher Raymond
Hannah Russell
James Shaw
Fiona Swapp
Andrew Tracey

Anglea Logan would like to dedicate this book to Adam G.M.B Logan.

Thank you to everyone who contributed to the Dear Nature Kickstarter to help make this first paperback edition happen. Thank you to everyone who bought the hardback in 2018–2019 and for your enthusiasm for the book which ultimately gave us the confidence to print this edition.

A special thanks to Reece Straw for his invaluable contribution during the campaign and for his interpretation of Dear Nature into a film. A special acknowledgement to those members of our community that read the letters for the book launch at Nottingham Contemporary and for the film recording.

Dear Nature
John Newling

Published by Beam Editions, UK
beameditions.uk
ISBN 978-1-9162759-2-8
Designed by Oliver Wood and Jonathan Casciani
Photography by James Gardiner

\ B /

ISBN 978-1-9162759-2-8

9 781916 275928 >